Mommy,
Where does Love come from?

by Nicole Pierce
Illustrations by Olha Tkachenko

This book is dedicated to my family-
My husband Gene (my biggest fan), I love you forever, and my children, Sarah, Matthew, Britin, Abigail,
Daniel and Maddison. I love you guys to the moon and back! You fill my life with so much joy and purpose!
Mommy loves you and so does Jesus!
A special thank you to my editor, Steve Johnson, for all of your help and encouragement!
I would also like to thank Olha Tkachenko for her incredible talent and beautiful artwork...

Text: Nicole Pierce; llustrations, design&layout: Olha Tkachenko, Edited by Tim Friesen (English), Natasha Kuznetsova, Julia Portnyagina (Ukrainian).
© Nicole Pierce, 2021 ISBN: 978-1-63821-438-0

"Mommy, I love you." Said Abigail.

"I love you too, sweetheart!" her Mommy replied.

"I know…but WHY?" Abigail asked.

"Because you're SPECIAL, one of a kind and my FAVORITE Abigail in the whole wide world!"

"What makes ME special?"

Her Mommy smiled and reached for her hand, together they walked over to a bench under a big oak tree and sat down.

"Well GOD made you UNIQUE. He knew you even before you were inside my tummy, he gave you CURLY hair, PRETTY blue eyes, a KIND smile, a loving HEART, and a curious mind. You are TRULY one of a kind. There is no one else that is just like YOU!"

"But you're like me." Abigail said.

Her Mommy laughed, "We are similar, yes, but not exactly the same."

"And HOW did GOD know me before I was in your tummy?!" Abigail exclaimed, wide eyed.

Her Mommy smiled again and lifted Abigail into her lap.

"Well, because he LOVED you and planned for you,

he knew EXACTLY who you'd be,

and who he wanted your MOMMY and DADDY to be too!"

"Lucky for US, He gave us YOU!"

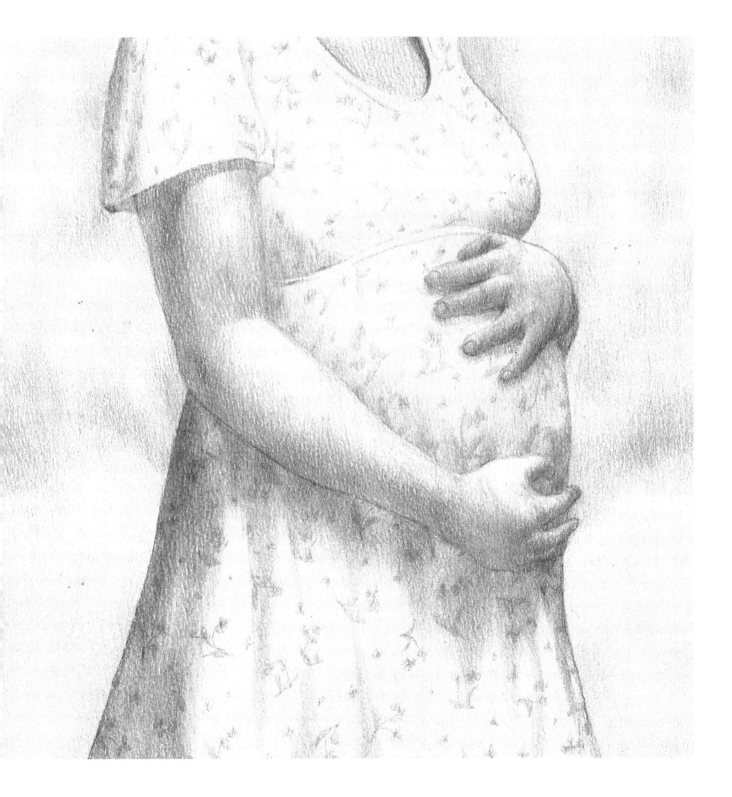

"How do we know GOD loves us?" Abigail asked.

"Because HE created us with LOVE in our HEARTS. We were made to LOVE Him, each other and ALL the people in the WORLD!"

"He's a WONDERFUL Father in Heaven and he sent his Son, JESUS, to die for us, so that anyone who BELIEVES in JESUS will also go to Heaven when they die."

Abigail looked up with sad eyes "I don't understand, Mommy. Why did Jesus have to die?"

Her mother said, "Because there were many people that sinned and broke God's laws, they didn't show love to one another, or to God and this made God sad. He sent his son, JESUS, who had never sinned, to die as a sacrifice for ALL of our sins, so that we could be FORGIVEN."

"Do WE follow God's Laws?" Abigail asked.

"We try our VERY best to follow His word, but EVERYONE has sinned. JESUS is the ONLY one who has never sinned, not even once!"

"We've all sinned? Even ME?"

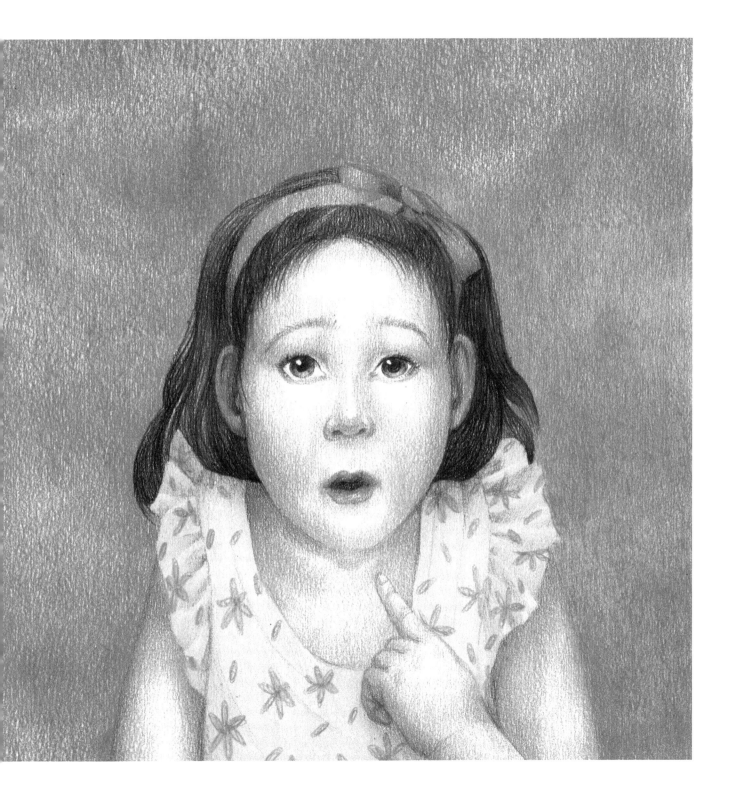

"Have you ever told a lie or disobeyed your Mom and Dad?"

Abigail looked down at the grass and whispered "Yes."

Her Mommy squeezed her in a hug and said, "Well, that's a sin, but we can tell God that we're SORRY and ask for his FORGIVENESS."

"And BECAUSE He loves us SO much, and sent JESUS to pay the price for the whole world's sins, WE can be FORGIVEN when we PRAY and ask him!"

"Is JESUS in HEAVEN?" Abigail asked.

"Yes." Her Mommy replied.

"And we'll go to HEAVEN too?"

"Yes, one day we will, because of what JESUS did for US."

"You're RIGHT Mommy, Jesus DOES love us, A LOT!"

With LOVE in her eyes, Abigail smiled at her mommy, bowed her head and began to pray;

Thank you, God, for making me!

Thank you for my family and for putting LOVE in our hearts.

Thank you for JESUS!

I'm SORRY for the times I've lied and sinned. Please forgive me and help me to keep your laws.

I love you SO, SO much, more than anything in THE WHOLE WORLD. Higher than the SKY and deeper than the SEA.

She opened her eyes and saw her mother SMILING at her, with HAPPY tears in her eyes, and together they said…

AMEN.

CPSIA information can be obtained
at www.ICGtesting.com
Printed in the USA
BVHW051206240621
610213BV00010B/772